From Zero to Hero

Sharon M. Draper

SCHOLASTIC INC.
New York   Toronto   London   Auckland   Sydney
Mexico City   New Delhi   Hong Kong

**Cover and interior illustrations by
Peter Spacek**

Copyright © 2001 by Scholastic Inc.
All rights reserved. Published by Scholastic Inc.
Printed in the U.S.A.

ISBN 0-439-31277-9

SCHOLASTIC, READ 180, and associated logos and designs are
trademarks and/or registered trademarks of Scholastic Inc.
LEXILE is a trademark of MetaMetrics, Inc.

3   4   5   6   7   8   9   10   23   10 09 08

Contents

1 Nothing Happens

"Ron, turn the TV off!" my mom said.

"But the best show is coming on now!" I told her.

"You watch too much TV!" she yelled. "Did you do your homework?" She always asks me that.

I always tell her the same thing. "I did it at school. I'll go to bed as soon as this show goes off, OK?"

She always lets me watch one more show. "OK, but no more," she said. "You watch too much TV!" she said one more time.

My favorite show is called *Street Hero*. On every show, someone has a really bad problem. Last week, a woman was hit by a car. On another show, a man had all his money taken after he was beat up. Every week, the Street Hero saves them. On tonight's show, the Street Hero saved a girl from a truck that was about to hit her.

I want to be a hero. But nothing ever happens on my street. Everybody drives slow. It's really boring. Dogs bark. Cats sleep. How can I be a hero living on a dumb street like that? Maybe a wild animal like a lion could escape from the zoo and nobody could catch it but me. That would be cool. I want to save somebody—maybe from a tiger or maybe from a train. But there are no tigers or trains around here.

My mom yelled one more time, "Turn that TV off now, Ron. Go to bed and get some sleep."

"OK, Mom," I said. I turned off the TV and picked up a video game. It was called "Space Hero." Space Hero kills space monsters and planet destroyers and evil robots. At level ten the planet blows up. I can get to level six on that game. I played Space Hero for two hours.

Space Hero saved the planet from the aliens and the world was safe until I got to level seven. I got sleepy. I went to bed and I dreamed of being a hero.

Have you ever wanted to be a hero? Why or why not?

2 Dream On

In my dream, a huge orange-and-black tiger walked down the halls of my school. He roared at all the kids. They ran from him and screamed. Even Big Bill was scared. Big Bill is really mean. Whenever he's in a fight, he wins. And he's always in a fight. Big Bill was afraid of the tiger in my dream. Everyone in the school was afraid, except for me.

The tiger hit my math teacher, Miss Turner, with his paw. He cut her face with his sharp claws. Then the tiger bit Miss Turner on the leg.

"Help me!" she screamed. She called to Big Bill. "Help me, Bill!" But Big Bill ran away. It was a crazy dream.

Then the tiger looked at Lisa Smith. Lisa

always looks good. She's the best-looking girl in my class. The tiger looked at Lisa like she was dinner. He walked closer to her. Lisa was scared. She was crying.

The tiger didn't see me. I walked up behind him and I grabbed his tail. I picked up the tiger and spun him around. Then I tossed him into his cage. Miss Turner was so happy, she said I never had to do math homework again.

Lisa was so happy that she wanted to kiss me. She walked over to me. She took my hand. She pulled me close to her. Her face was very close to mine.

"Get up, Ron! You're late for school!" That was when my mom woke me up and messed up my dream. It was just my luck.

What do you think would have happened next in Ron's dream?

3 Total Zero

I was in a bad mood all day. I was sleepy and mad. In math class Miss Turner was in a bad mood, too.

"Where is your homework, Ron?" she asked me.

"I left it at home," I told her.

"That's a zero for today!" she said. "You will do four pages of homework tonight to make up for this!" she yelled.

I didn't say anything, but I hoped a tiger would walk into the room. This time I would not save her.

Lisa Smith looked good again today. She had on a new yellow top. She looked like lemon candy. But she laughed when Miss

Turner yelled at me. I wondered if tigers like lemon candy.

I fell asleep in history class. The room was dark because Mr. Tang was showing a movie. It was about explorers who left their homes and sailed on ships to discover new places in the world. Mr. Tang said they were heroes. But they lived a long time ago.

I don't think there are any new places left to discover. Explorers have been to the bottom of the ocean, and they have been to the top of the highest mountains. They have even been to the moon. Maybe the only place left to explore is way out in space. I fell asleep dreaming about being Space Hero.

I dreamed I was on a space ship, and I was the captain. Bright stars were all around me. It looked like a space movie I saw on TV. A ship from another planet was about to attack. Blue waves of space gunfire filled the sky.

My crew was afraid, but I was not. "Be brave," I called out to them.

But they ran to the bottom of the space ship. Big Bill was my first mate. "Stay with me, Bill.

You're strong and can fight this battle with me." But Big Bill ran with the others.

I stood alone, facing the attack. The waves of space gunfire shook the ship, but I never gave up. I sped my ship to safety. I was the hero.

Soon I saw a small planet. I landed my ship and went out to explore. I was near a sandy beach, like the ones you see on a TV show. I could hear birds. Standing on the beach was Lisa Smith. She had on a yellow bathing suit. She was smiling at me and waving. I ran across the sand to her. She had her arms out to hug me.

"Hey, Ron! The bell rang, stupid! Go to your next class!" It was Lisa Smith. She was laughing at me. I woke up and looked around. The movie was over. The room was almost empty. Mr. Tang was laughing, too.

How do you think Ron felt when he woke up?

4 Beaten Down

After school I missed the last bus home. So I had to walk. It had not been a good day. I had too much homework. My teachers were mean. Lisa Smith had laughed at me—twice. Just then Big Bill gave me a shove.

"Give me your jacket," he said.

"You must be crazy!" I told him.

"Give me your jacket," he said again.

"No!"

"Then I'll have to beat you and take it!" he said. He shoved me again.

I shoved back, but it only made him mad. He knocked me down. My book bag was heavy and I fell in the dirt. I grabbed his leg and pulled him down. He hit me in the face.

My nose was bleeding. My jeans were torn. I was angry. I tried to hit Big Bill back, but he was too fast. He grabbed my jacket and ran away. I sat in the dirt. I felt like dirt. It had been a very bad day.

I picked up my book bag, brushed off my clothes, and walked away. My mother was going to be very angry about the jacket. Some hero I turned out to be. I couldn't even save my own clothing.

If you were Ron's mother, what would you say about the jacket?

5 Real-Life Rescue

I walked for many blocks feeling weak and stupid. I was glad that no one had seen me get beat up. I was more than halfway home. The streets were very quiet. As I turned the corner, I did not notice the smoke at first. But something smelled bad, like the smell when my mother burns dinner. Then I looked up and saw that the yellow house on the corner had smoke coming from one of the windows. It was thick black smoke. The yellow house on the corner was on fire!

"Fire!" I yelled. But no one was around. The street was empty.

I ran to the yellow house. I beat on the front door. It was warm when I touched it. I rang the door bell again and again. The smoke was getting thicker.

I ran to the neighbor's house and beat on the door. No one was home. I ran to a house across the street, then to another one. No one was home anywhere. I was all alone on the street. Finally a car passed by and stopped.

"Please call for help! This house is on fire!" I yelled. The man picked up his cell phone to call, but it had no power.

"I'll find a pay phone and call 911 for you. I promise," the man said. He drove away quickly.

I ran to the back of the house. Smoke was coming from those windows too. I heard a dog barking. I looked up, and there in an upstairs window stood a little girl and her dog. She was crying. The dog was barking. The window was open, and it looked like the little girl was trying to get out.

"Wait! I'll help you!" I yelled.

The little girl said nothing. She just kept crying.

I looked around for a ladder. Then I looked for a rope. I saw nothing that could help me except a tree. It grew close to the window where the little girl stood. I climbed the tree and tried to reach the little girl. She ran back into the house. The dog stood there and barked at me.

"Come here, little girl," I said. "I want to help you."

"I'm scared," the girl said. "I want my mommy."

"I'm scared, too," I told her. "Where is your mommy?"

"Mommy won't wake up," the little girl said. Then she started crying harder.

I tried to get closer to the window, but I couldn't. I could see smoke behind the girl and the dog. I did not know what to do, but I knew I had to hurry.

"If you come to the window, I will help you," I said to her. "What is your name?"

"Penny," the little girl said.

"Well, Penny, we have to hurry, or your dog will get hurt."

"I don't want Rocky to get hurt," Penny said.

"Come closer to me," I said. "Let's save Rocky."

The little girl stood by the window. "Give Rocky to me," I said. She held the dog in her arms and helped him out the window. I took Rocky and set him gently in the tree. Rocky

did not move. He was scared too. Then I reached for the little girl.

"Come on, Penny. We are going to climb down this tree, OK?"

"OK. But what about Rocky?"

"As soon I get you down, I'll go and get Rocky. He's a smart dog. He won't move."

"What about my mommy?" Penny asked.

"As soon I get you down, we will look for your mom, OK?"

I didn't know how I would ever find her mother in all that smoke and fire, but I had to get Penny out of that window first.

Penny gave me both her hands, and she leaned out far enough so I could reach her. I helped her out of the window and onto the tree. I took her down slowly, then I went back and got Rocky.

I looked back at the house. Black smoke, dark and thick, rolled from the windows. I could see bright red flames near the roof. I was really scared. Penny started crying again.

By that time, the fire trucks had come. Firemen ran everywhere with hoses and lots of noise. I held Penny's hand while we watched the firemen spray water on the flames.

"There's my mommy!" Penny cried with joy. The firemen had found Penny's mom in the burning house. She had passed out while trying to find Penny. But she was fine now. She ran to Penny and hugged her and cried. Rocky barked a lot.

People from the TV news came and took pictures of the burning house, and of Penny, her mom, Rocky, and even me.

I watched them put the fire out, then I headed for home. I was very late, and I knew my mom would be mad.

"Where have you been?" my mom asked as soon as I walked in the door. She had that angry mom look on her face. "Why are you so dirty? And why is your shirt torn? Have you been fighting? Where's your jacket?"

When my mom gets mad, she asks lots of questions. But she never lets me answer. I wonder why.

"You smell like smoke!" my mother said then. "What have you been doing?"

"I climbed a tree," I said at first. I know that sounded dumb. "It was right next to a house that was on fire," I said. "There was this little girl and she . . . ," I tried to tell my mom but she interrupted me before I could finish.

"You could have been hurt!" she said. "Why would you climb a tree next to a burning house?"

It was another one of those questions that she really didn't want me to answer. So I gave up. I was tired and wanted to take a bath. "The house was on fire. I watched them put it out. I'm OK," I told her.

She looked at me like I had soup for brains. But she didn't ask any more questions. I did not tell her about the jacket.

I ate my dinner, did my homework, and went to bed. I did not watch TV. I fell fast asleep, but I must have been too tired to dream.

How did Ron convince Penny to climb out the window?

6 My Hero!

The next morning, my mom woke me up for school.

"Ron! Get up! Look at this!" Mom sounded happy.

I rubbed my eyes and looked at what she had in her hand. It was the morning newspaper. On the front page was a picture of me. My face was dirty and I looked surprised. The paper said, "Hero Saves Girl From Burning House." The story told about how I had saved Penny and Rocky.

My mom asked, "Why didn't you tell me? This is on the TV morning news, too. Everyone is talking about it. You're a hero, Ron!"

"I tried to tell you last night," I said.

"I was angry last night. I'm sorry I didn't listen," Mom said.

"I didn't think it was a big deal," I said.

"Well, it is. It's a very big deal. I am very proud of you, son."

The phone rang then. It was Lisa Smith. "I saw your picture in the paper," she said to me. "You're a hero, Ron!"

Lisa Smith called me! My heart was beating fast.

"I'll see you in school," she said softly.

"Yeah, sure," I said. I wondered if she was going to wear yellow today. I jumped out of bed to take a shower. I had a feeling that it was going to be a very good day.

How do you think Ron feels about himself now?

Meet the Author

I'm a dreamer, a creator, a visionary. I see rainbows where others see only rain, and possibilities when others see only problems.

I'm an author and a poet. I love to write. Words flow from my fingertips, and my heart beats rapidly with excitement as an idea becomes a reality on the paper in front of me.

I'm a teacher. I have always encouraged in my students a love of learning and a desire for excellence. I tell them, "If you want to be a spinner of words, you must first gather them into your heart by reading."

I learned to dream through reading. I learned to create dreams through writing. And I learned to help young dreamers through teaching. I shall always be a dreamer.

To find out more about me and my books, visit my Web site at: **www.sharondraper.com.**
—*Sharon M. Draper*